S0-AXN-569

This Book
Belongs To:

Geckos Slide and Peek

A Look-and-Find Adventure in Hawai'i

Illustrated by
Jon J. Murakami

BeachHouse

Across the islands
every day
geckos gather
to work and play

at the beach,

 in the park,

on carnival rides
after dark.

Geckos roll sushi,

make shave ice,

play Hawaiian music,

eat poi and rice.

Dozens and dozens of objects hide
inside these pages so use your eyes
and find all kinds of different things
like a diving monkey or floating ring.

Two special geckos, Slide and Peek, hide among the things you seek.

Slide: wears a green T-shirt with a yellow "S" on it. Slide is always sliding on something.

Peek: has a white plumeria behind her ear and wears a pink T-shirt with a "P" on it. Peek is always peeking behind something.

Find them both and just for fun find ALL these things one by one. Each can be found on every page search high and low (whatever your age).

Honu

Sleeping gecko

Christmas gecko

Toy robot

Purple surfboard with yellow stripe

Reading gecko

Gecko who keeps losing his balloons

The letters that spell GECKO

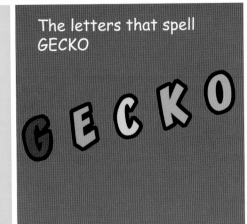

Ninja gecko

Gecko holding rainbow shave ice that's in the order of red, yellow, blue.

'Ukulele

Ghost gecko

Pineapple

Hibiscus

Gecko wearing a blue fishing hat

Gecko wearing a red baseball cap

Gecko wearing funny pants

And then in case you're still not through, we've hidden more stuff just for you. Read the list of things to seek on every page, just take a peek!

Geckos on the Beach

Try to find: A cupcake, two crabs, a sandman, a frog.

An octopus, a Jet Ski, a lock, a dog.

Deep Sea Geckos

Try to find: A pufferfish, an eel, a camera, an X.

A hermit crab, a monkey, a lost treasure chest.

Gecko Sushi

Try to find: A drum, a spatula, a tube of wasabi.

An eight-ball, a blender, a pink pot of tea.

Shave Ice Shop

Try to find: A lightbulb, a chalkboard, a red heart,

SHAVE ICE

a rainbow. Building blocks, bacon, an avocado.

A Day in the Park
Try to find: A hula hoop, a helicopter, a bear, a bee.

A white house, a question mark, a flying frisbee.

Hana Hou!

Try to find: Scissors, a tuba, headphones, a fan.

3-D glasses, a top hat, an angry policeman.

Night at the Carnival

Try to find: A cowboy, a watergun, a pirate, a trumpet

A lollipop, a unicorn, a butterfly net.

Gecko Lū'au

Try to find: A chicken, a clock, a roasted marshmallow

Two balloons, a mongoose, a superhero.

You might think
you're done, but no!
There's more for you
to find, let's go!

Twelve more objects
hide throughout
all the pages,
all about.

So start again,
just take a peek.
We know you'll find
the things you seek.

Angry gecko

Humuhumunukunukuapua'a

Cool gecko

Gecko wearing a black hat

Pair of blue slippers

Shaka

Gecko with red umbrella

Gecko wearing a gray cap

Gecko wearing a straw hat

Gecko with purple flower in her hair

Purple lei

Gecko wearing green ti leaf hat

About the Illustrator

Jon J. Murakami is a freelance cartoonist born, raised, and still living in Hawai'i, best known for his line of Local Kine greeting cards, which depicts humorous occasions and holidays in Hawai'i.

Jon has illustrated several local children books: the Gecko series of BeachHouse board books, *If You Were a Superhero in Hawai'i*, *My Dog has Flies*, *Going to the Zoo in Hawai'i*, *The Winged Tiger and the Dragons of Hawai'i*, *Kula and the Old 'Ukulele*, *The Original Poi Cats on O'ahu*, and a cookbook with L&L co-founder Eddie Flores Jr. titled *$266 Million Winning Lottery Recipes: L&L Hawaiian Barbecue Cookbook*.

His comic strips include "Online Aloha" featured on the Hawai'i TimeWarner Oceanic site, "Generation Gap" featured twice a month in the Japanese-American newspaper *The Hawai'i Herald*, and "Calabash" seen in the *Honolulu Star-Advertiser* every 3 weeks.

He also draws self-published comic books such as "Gordon Rider," a parody of Japanese superhero television shows from the '70s, starring the worst superhero ever in Hawai'i. A newly released comic called "The Ara-rangers" parodies *Power Rangers* using Arare as a theme.

And despite all of this, Jon still finds time to play games on his iPhone.

Other BeachHouse books by Jon J. Murakami

Psst..... some of the geckos in Jon's board books appear in this book!

Copyright © 2013 by BeachHouse Publishing
Illustrations copyright © 2013 by Jon J. Murakami

No part of this book may be reproduced in any form or by any electronic or mechanical means, including information storage and retrieval devices or systems, without prior written permission from the publisher, except that brief passages may be quoted for reviews.
All rights reserved.

ISBN-10: 1-933067-59-4
ISBN-13: 978-1-933067-59-9
Library of Congress Control Number: 2013945266
Text and Design by Jane Gillespie

Second Printing, January 2016

BeachHouse Publishing, LLC
PO Box 5464
Kāne'ohe, Hawai'i 96744
info@beachhousepublishing.com
www.beachhousepublishing.com
Printed in China